PLANET HOCKEY

FIRST STAR OF THE GAME

PLANET HOCKEY

FIRST STAR OF THE GAME

WRITTEN BY
J. TORRES

ILLUSTRATED BY
TIM LEVINS

Scholastic Canada Ltd.
Toronto New York London Auckland Sydney
Mexico City New Delhi Hong Kong Buenos Aires

Scholastic Canada Ltd.
604 King Street West, Toronto, Ontario M5V 1E1, Canada

Scholastic Inc.
557 Broadway, New York, NY 10012, USA

Scholastic Australia Pty Limited
PO Box 579, Gosford, NSW 2250, Australia

Scholastic New Zealand Limited
Private Bag 94407, Botany, Manukau 2163, New Zealand

Scholastic Children's Books
Euston House, 24 Eversholt Street, London NW1 1DB, UK

www.scholastic.ca

Library and Archives Canada Cataloguing in Publication
Title: Planet hockey : first star of the game / J. Torres ;
illustrated by Tim Levins.
Names: Torres, J., 1969- author. | Levins, Tim, illustrator
Identifiers: Canadiana 20200191004 | ISBN 9781443128896 (softcover)
Subjects: LCGFT: Graphic novels.
Classification: LCC PN6733.T67 P53 2020 | DDC j741.5/971—dc23

Colour assist by Sigmund Torre.

6 5 4 3 2 1   Printed in Malaysia   108   20 21 22 23 24 25

For my late mother, Guia, who was a big fan of the Canadiens. She especially loved Carey Price, one of the inspirations for Isaac in this story.

— J.T.

To Shari and James — thanks so much for your love and support. I couldn't have done this without you.

— T.L.

CONTENTS

INTRODUCTION 1

YOU'VE GOAT IT ALL WRONG 4

THERE IS NO "I" IN BEAM 23

ICE TO SEE YOU 55

HOW THE ROOKIE CRUMBLES 79

THE PUCK STOPS HERE 99

THE GOAT ONE 114

LIKE MOST KIDS, ISAAC HAS HAD HIS SHARE OF ACCIDENTS.

LAST SEASON, ISAAC HAD AN UNFORTUNATE ACCIDENT THAT LED TO THIS SEASON'S UNLIKELY INCIDENT. IT ALL STARTED IN THE PLAYOFFS.

GO, ICEMAN!

ISAAC'S #1 FAN

YOU CAN DO IT!

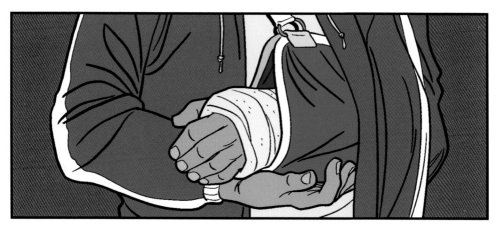

I SUCK. I COST US THE GAME.

YOU CAUGHT AN EDGE, SON. IT HAPPENS.

EVERYONE HATES ME. I HATE ME.

NOBODY **HATES** YOU, ISAAC.

I'M **NEVER** PLAYING HOCKEY EVER AGAIN.

4

...HITS A LOT HARDER...

...AND IS PLAYED A LITTLE BIT...

...DIFFERENTLY?

ON GALAXIA THE MORE YOU **LOSE**...

...THE MORE **TAXES** YOU PAY!

AND THE TEAM WITH THE **WORST** STATS ALSO CLEANS EVERYONE ELSE'S EQUIPMENT!

SO SAYETH THE SUPREME LEADER OF GALAXIA, THE BOSS OF EVERYONE (AND SELF-PROCLAIMED #1 HOCKEY FAN IN THE UNIVERSE), **EMPEROR MAD MAROON!**

8

THE GALAXIAN HOCKEY LEAGUE, OR GHL, HAS AN ANNUAL TOURNAMENT. FOR THE LAST TEN LUNAR CYCLES THE WORST TEAM HAS BEEN THE PODS.

LOSER!

PAF!

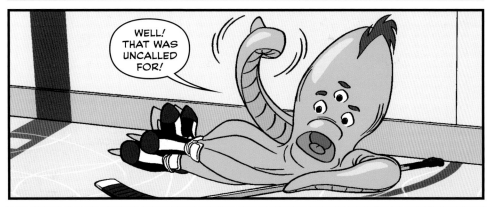

WELL! THAT WAS UNCALLED FOR!

WE CANNOT KEEP LOSING LIKE THIS! ZEAZIDE IS RUNNING OUT OF ZANDOLLARS TO PAY THE HOCKEY TAX.

HEY THERE! SKOU7 HERE IS A GREAT ROBOT, ESPECIALLY FOR THAT LOW, LOW PRICE.

IT CAN FLY A SPACESHIP. IT'S A COMPETENT CONTRACT NEGOTIATOR. IT CAN MAKE GRILLED-CHEESE SANDWICHES!

SKOU7 LOOKS A LITTLE OLD. HOW UP TO DATE IS THE GPS?

WELL, PLUTO **WAS** STILL A PLANET THE LAST TIME ITS GALACTIC POSITIONING SOFTWARE WAS UPDATED.

SKOU7'S GPS IS **TOTALLY** UP TO DATE! THE BEST! MOSTLY... ...A LITTLE...

...ANYWAY, YOU WON'T FIND ANYTHING CHEAPER IN ALL OF GALAXIA!

I HOPE SKOU7 FINDS THE HOCKEY GOAT FOR US.

I HOPE THE GPS WORKS.

AND THUS, SKOU7 WAS TASKED TO RECRUIT THE BEST HOCKEY PLAYER IN THE COSMOS: THE HOCKEY GOAT FROM PLANET GRF3.

THE HOCKEY GOAT HAS WON SIX COSMIC HOCKEY LEAGUE CHAMPIONSHIPS AS THE CAPTAIN OF A TEAM CALLED THE 789S.

O-EM-GEE

HOCKEY GOAT

789s

THE HOCKEY GOAT HAS PLAYED HOCKEY EVER SINCE HE WAS A KID...

...BUT HE IS **NOT** THIS KID. THE ONE CALLED ISAAC FROM PLANET EARTH.

GRF3.

ON EARTH, ISAAC BECAME THE GREATEST OF ALL TIME IN THE MULTIPLAYER ONLINE GAME SHOT, SHORT FOR SUPER HOCKEY ONLINE TOURNAMENT.

SO, ALL OF THESE "GOATS" AND LEAGUES, ONLINE OR OTHERWISE, CAUSED THE CONFUSION THAT EVENTUALLY LED TO THE UNLIKELY INCIDENT.

HMM... WHERE IS THAT ROBOT?

13

14

BYE!

HEY... ISAAC?

WAIT UP!

I'M LILY. YOU'RE SUPPOSED TO SHOW ME AROUND.

OH, RIGHT.

LATER...

...AND NOT AT A DOCTOR TEETH APPOINTMENT...

WOW. SHE'S GOOD.

YEAH, REALLY GOOD!

WHY DON'T YOU GO OUT THERE AND PLAY WITH THEM?

I HAVE TO... YOU KNOW, DO HOMEWORK THINGS!

LOOK, ISAAC, IT'S BEEN MONTHS. EVERYONE'S FORGOTTEN ABOUT IT. TIME FOR YOU TO GET OVER IT, TOO.

YOU HAVE TO GET BACK IN THE GAME SOMEDAY, KIDDO.

DON'T YOU *MISS* PLAYING HOCKEY?

Chapter 2:
THERE IS NO "I" IN BEAM

WHERE AM I?

HOW DID I GET HERE?

GREETINGS, THE GOAT!

WHAAAA

DO NOT BE ALARMED, THE GOAT. I AM SKOU7, SENT BY THE PODS TO BRING YOU TO GALAXIA.

WHAT IS GOING ON HERE?

YOU SHOULD BE COMFORTABLE IN YOUR STASIS CAPSULE FOR THE JOURNEY. DO NOT HESITATE TO LET ME KNOW IF YOU NEED ANYTHING, SUCH AS A GRILLED-CHEESE SANDWICH.

I WILL DO **WHAT?**

YOU WILL PLAY HOCKEY IN THE GHL, FOR THE ZEAZIDE PODS.

WAIT -- **YOU** ARE RECRUITING **ME** TO PLAY HOCKEY FOR SOME TEAM?

NO, NO, NO. I DON'T PLAY ANYMORE. AT LEAST NOT **REAL** HOCKEY... NOT SINCE ...

ANYWAY, YOU DON'T WANT ME. YOU WANT A **REAL** PLAYER, SOMEONE GOOD ... LIKE MY NEW NEIGHBOUR LILY!

HMM ... SCANNING FOR THE LILY!

WOW. THE LILY IS A GOOD NETMINDER.

REALLY GOOD. THE PODS NEED A REALLY GOOD NETMINDER.

PLEASE, THE LILY. ALLOW ME TO EXPLAIN.

I COME FROM PLANET GALAXIA, WHICH IS ONE WARP JUMP AND TWO SLEEPS AWAY. ON GALAXIA WE HAVE AN ANNUAL HOCKEY TOURNAMENT.

I LOVE HOCKEY, DREAM ROBOT!

SO DOES THE EMPEROR OF GALAXIA. PERHAPS THE ONLY THING HE LOVES MORE THAN HOCKEY ARE TAXES. THUS, THE TEAMS MUST PAY A HOCKEY TAX WITH THE WORST TEAM PAYING THE MOST.

THAT DOESN'T SEEM FAIR!

THE WORST TEAM MUST ALSO CLEAN THE OTHER TEAMS' STINKY EQUIPMENT.

THAT'S JUST GROSS!

QUITE. THUS, I HAVE BEEN TASKED BY THE PODS, THE LAST-PLACE TEAM IN THE GHL, TO RECRUIT PLAYERS TO HELP THEM WIN. THEY CANNOT AFFORD THE HOCKEY TAX AND ARE ABOUT TO GO BROKE.

WELL, THAT'S JUST SAD.

27

YOU ARE WILLING TO HELP THE PODS AND PLAY FOR THEIR TEAM? TO COMPENSATE YOU, I AM AUTHORIZED TO OFFER A BEACH VACATION AND ALL-YOU-CAN-EAT GARBAGE.

UM ... I DON'T EAT GARBAGE.

BUT I **WAS** JUST SAYING THAT I'D RATHER BE **ANYWHERE** ELSE BUT HOGTOWN!

ARE YOU SERIOUS, LILY?

MAY I GET YOU A GRILLED-CHEESE SANDWICH?

LET'S JUST GO WITH IT, ISAAC ...

IT'S A DEAL, SPACE DREAM ROBOT!

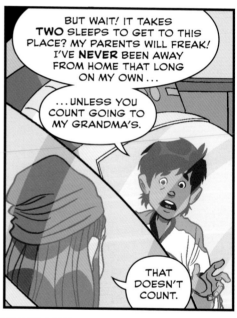

BUT WAIT! IT TAKES **TWO** SLEEPS TO GET TO THIS PLACE? MY PARENTS WILL FREAK! I'VE **NEVER** BEEN AWAY FROM HOME THAT LONG ON MY OWN ...

... UNLESS YOU COUNT GOING TO MY GRANDMA'S.

THAT DOESN'T COUNT.

NO ONE NEED WORRY OR "FREAK." THE WARP JUMP INVOLVES SOME SPATIAL-TEMPORAL DISPLACEMENT THAT, WHEN INITIATED IN REVERSE, RETURNS YOU MERE MOMENTS AFTER DEPARTURE.

I'M NOT SURE WHAT THAT MEANS.

I THINK HE'S SAYING WE WON'T GET GROUNDED?

ONE WARP JUMP AND TWO SLEEPS LATER...

ISAAC, WE'RE NOT IN HOGTOWN ANYMORE.

I FEEL LIKE DOROTHY IN *THE WIZARD OF OZ.*

I FEEL LIKE PUKING. IS THAT THE SPATIAL-TEMPORAL DISPLACEMENT THING?

YOU'RE REALLY INTO THIS, HUH?

LOOK, IF THIS IS A DREAM, I'LL WAKE UP AND TELL YOU ALL ABOUT IT.

IF IT'S ALL REAL, THEN IT'S ONE OF THOSE ONCE-IN-A-LIFETIME OPPORTUNITIES.

LIKE MY MOM'S NEW JOB, WHICH IS WHY WE HAD TO MOVE.

AND I WOULDN'T BE HERE IF MY MOM DIDN'T TAKE THAT JOB!

YEAH, A "ONCE-IN-A-LIFETIME OPPORTUNITY" ...TO EMBARRASS MYSELF ON A TOTALLY DIFFERENT PLANET...

GLUUBLY, GLUB GLUB! GLUB GLUBBY GLUBBY GLUB!

EXCUSE ME?

APOLOGIES! I FORGOT TO GIVE YOU YOUR EAR WERMS.

EAR WORMS?

YES, THEY WILL ALLOW YOU TO UNDERSTAND THE DIFFERENT LANGUAGES SPOKEN ON GALAXIA.

WELL, THAT'S COOL. BUT I HOPE THEY TASTE BETTER THAN YOUR SANDWICHES.

NO, NO. YOU DO NOT INGEST THEM. THEY ARE FOR PUTTING IN YOUR EAR.

OHHHH! AND ALSO, EWW.

IT TICKLES!

GLUB ... AND AS MAYOR OF ZEAZIDE, I EXTEND GREETINGS TO THE GOAT AND THE LILY, OUR **AWFUL** HOCKEY TEAM'S NEW PLAYERS!

SO, IT IS OUR SINCEREST WISH THAT OUR NEW STAR PLAYER, THE GOAT, WILL TAKE US THERE!

IT IS THE DREAM OF EVERY CITIZEN TO **NOT** LOSE EVERY GAME OF EVERY TOURNAMENT. AND SINCE WE ARE AT THE VERY BOTTOM, WE CAN ONLY GO **UP** FROM HERE.

NO PRESSURE.

DID HE JUST CALL HIS OWN TEAM AWFUL?

WOULD YOU CARE TO SAY A FEW WORDS, THE GOAT?

ME? UM ...

THANK YOU? WE LOOK FORWARD TO ... NOT LOSING? AND TO HELPING ... MAKE YOUR DREAM COME TRUE?

SO ...

LET'S GO ...

... UP?

OKAY, WHERE'S THE COACH? I REALLY NEED TO TALK TO THE COACH.

WE HAVE NOT HAD A COACH IN TWO SEASONS.

THREE SEASONS.

WHAT?

WE HAVE ALSO BEEN TAKING TURNS IN NET AS WE HAVE NOT HAD A PROPER NETMINDER IN THREE SEASONS.

FOUR SEASONS.

I GOT THE GOALIE THING, NO PROBLEM.

MY JOB HERE IS DONE.

VERY EXPENSIVE.

WE COULD NOT AFFORD A ROBOT COACH SO WE INVESTED IN A ROBOT SCOUT TO FIND US THE GOAT TO BE OUR CAPTAIN!

AND TO FIND ANYONE ELSE WHO COULD HELP US, LIKE THE LILY!

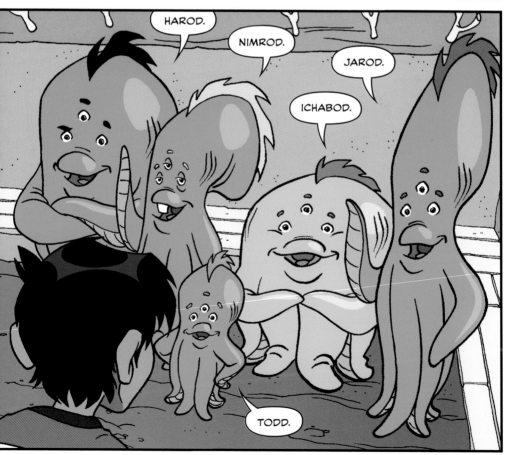

HAROD.

NIMROD.

JAROD.

ICHABOD.

TODD.

...I THINK MAYBE... YOU NEED A **COACH** MORE THAN A CAPTAIN...

...AND I **CAN'T** REALLY BE BOTH.

SO, I'LL BE YOUR NEW COACH!

I'M SURE **ONE** OF YOU GUYS WILL MAKE A GOOD CAPTAIN. LET'S TAKE IT FROM THERE, OKAY?

OUR FIRST PRACTICE IS SCHEDULED FOR SECOND SUNRISE ON THE MORROW!

SECOND SUNRISE?

HERE COME THE SUNS...

AND HERE COME THE PODS!

I HOPE THEY GOT A GOOD SLEEP IN THEIR UNDERWATER BEDS.

THIS IS TOTALLY NOT WEIRD, RIGHT?

PLAYING HOCKEY WITH OCTOPUS-LIKE CREATURES? NOT WEIRD AT ALL!

OH MAN... THEY'RE REALLY SLOW ON THE SAND! I HOPE THEY DO BETTER ON ICE.

WE... ARE COMING!

ALMOST... UGH...

WE MIGHT HAVE TO WORK ON SOME BASIC SKILLS, "COACH."

OBVIOUSLY.

YOU'RE NOT SUITING UP?

UM. I DIDN'T BRING MY GEAR.

NEITHER DID I, SILLY! BUT SOMEONE LEFT A BAG OF STUFF FOR ME IN THE LOCKER ROOM.

DIDN'T YOU GET ONE?

OH... UM, I GUESS I MISSED IT? WHY DON'T YOU WARM UP WITH THE PODS? DO SOME LAPS OR SOMETHING WHILE I GO CHECK...

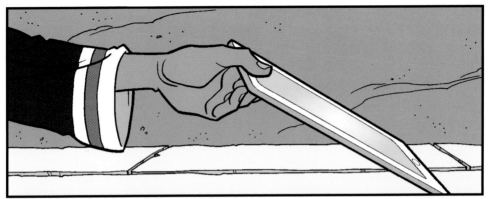

HEY! GHL TEAMS.

THE STREEK?

THE STALKS?

THESE GUYS LOOK SCARY!

ISAAC! **WHERE** HAVE YOU BEEN? WHAT'S TAKING SO LONG?

WE DID LAPS, AND I EVEN LET EVERYONE TAKE A FEW SHOTS AT ME! WE'RE WAITING ON **YOU.**

LOOK AT THIS.

WHAT IS IT?

THE GHL TOURNAMENT SCHEDULE. WE'RE PLAYING THE SPORKS IN THE LAST GAME OF THE FIRST ROUND.

AWW, THE SPORKS LOOK ADORABLE!

IF YOU SAY SO. BUT LOOK AT THE **OTHER** TEAMS!

YIKES!

THE AMPHS? THE CRAG? THE BLAST? WHAT ARE THOSE THINGS? WHERE ARE THEIR ARMS? OR LEGS?

WE SHOULD DEFINITELY GO TO THE OTHER GAMES AND CHECK OUT THE COMPETITION.

WHY BOTHER? WE'RE NOT EVEN GOING TO MAKE IT OUT OF THE **FIRST** ROUND, LILY. NOT WITH **THIS** TEAM.

NOT WITH **THAT** ATTITUDE! COME ON, COACH. I GET NERVOUS BEFORE BIG GAMES TOO.

BUT WE SAID WE'D HELP THESE GUYS. THE EMPEROR HAS TAKEN ALMOST EVERYTHING FROM THEM, AND WHAT THEY HAVE LEFT THEY WANT TO GIVE TO **US**?

WE **HAVE** TO HELP THEM. WE HAVE TO AT LEAST TRY. COME ON, JUST GO WITH IT.

≥SIGH≤

OKAY. I'LL BE OUT THERE IN A MINUTE.

IF ONLY THIS WAS A *SHOT* TOURNAMENT...

HEYYY...WAIT A MINUTE.

WHAT? YOU STILL HAVEN'T PUT ON YOUR SKATES OR ANYTHING!

THERE'S A WHITEBOARD APP ON THIS TABLET THAT **ALMOST** PLAYS LIKE A VIDEO GAME!

SO WHAT? THERE ARE OCTOPUS-LIKE ALIENS ON THE ICE WHO CAN **ALMOST** PLAY HOCKEY!

I NEED A MONITOR!

51

HE IS GOOD!

VERY GOOD!

SO, WHO ARE MY FORWARDS?

THE TRICK IS THINKING ONE OR TWO MOVES AHEAD...

...SETTING UP THE PLAY.

MAYBE WE SHOULD STICK TO THE BASICS.

TOO BAD THERE'S NO SUCH THING AS WATER HOCKEY. REMEMBER HOW SMOOTH THEY WERE ON THE WATER?

A COUPLE OF THE PODS HAVE A DECENT SHOT, BUT IT'S GOING TO TAKE MORE THAN THAT TO WIN.

WE NEED A CAPTAIN. IZOD, MAYBE?

MAYBE "THE GOAT" SHOULD GET OUT THERE AND SHOW THEM HOW IT'S DONE.

I WOULD BUT...

...I'M STARTING TO FEEL QUEASY AGAIN. I THINK I CAUGHT A BUG?

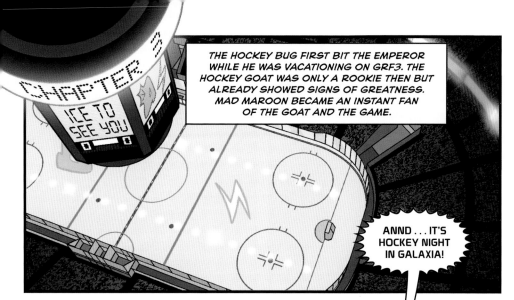

THE HOCKEY BUG FIRST BIT THE EMPEROR WHILE HE WAS VACATIONING ON GRF3. THE HOCKEY GOAT WAS ONLY A ROOKIE THEN BUT ALREADY SHOWED SIGNS OF GREATNESS. MAD MAROON BECAME AN INSTANT FAN OF THE GOAT AND THE GAME.

ANND . . . IT'S HOCKEY NIGHT IN GALAXIA!

HERE WE ARE FOR GAME ONE OF OUR ANNUAL TOURNAMENT, WHERE IT'S THE STREEK OF MOUNT KRAKOOM VERSUS THE AMPHIBIA AMPHS.

WE ARE WAITING FOR THE OPENING REMARKS FROM HIS EXCELLENCY, EMPEROR MAROON.

THIS IS REALLY EXCITING!

WE'RE **NOT** HERE TO HAVE FUN! WE'RE HERE TO STUDY THE OTHER TEAMS, LEARN THE WAY THE GAME IS PLAYED HERE, AND MAYBE--

FLEANUTS! ROCKCORN! MACKEREL JACKS!

OOH! I'LL TRY SOME MACKEREL JACKS!

WHAT? I THOUGHT YOUR STOMACH WASN'T FEELING WELL?

UH... RIGHT. MAYBE I SHOULDN'T EAT ANYTHING.

MACKEREL JACKS SOUND GROSS ANYWAY!

YEAH... TOTALLY GROSS.

RUMBLE

HEY... IS THAT THE EMPEROR?

NOW, I HEAR THAT OUR LAST-PLACE TEAM HAS BROUGHT IN SOME ALIEN . . . RINGERS?

WELL, THEY DON'T LOOK LIKE MUCH. BUT I SUPPOSE YOU GET WHAT YOU PAY FOR.

MAYBE THE PODS SHOULD **STOP** LOSING SO THEY CAN AFFORD A ROBOT COACH OR WHATEVER TO **HELP** THEM STOP LOSING? BUT REALLY, IT'S NOT ABOUT WINNING OR LOSING. IT'S HOW YOU PLAY THE GAME . . .

. . . TO ENTERTAIN **ME**, YOUR EMPEROR!

USE RINGERS IF YOU MUST, BUT DON'T BORE ME BECAUSE WHEN I GET BORED . . .

IT'S TEN MINUTES IN . . . **THE PENALTY BOX OF PAIN!**

59

AND WITH ONLY SECONDS ON THE CLOCK, HE SHOOTS...

...AND IT'S A GLOVE SAVE BY SKYDEN!

IT'S A SHUTOUT!

THEIR NETMINDER IS EXCEPTIONAL.

QUITE EXCEPTIONAL.

THE STREEK WILL BE HARD TO BEAT.

HEY! WE CAN STILL CATCH THE NEXT GAME!

YEESH. THEY LOOK LIKE A FUN BUNCH!

THE MUCK.

THEY COME FROM A PLACE CALLED CROOD. I'VE NEVER SEEN ONE SMILE.

DO YOU...

...DO YOU SMELL THAT?

EWW! WHAT IS THAT STINK?

I THINK... I THINK IT'S THEM.

THE BLAST!

SO...THE STREEK HAVE ELECTRIC EEL POWERS AND THESE GUYS HAVE STINKBUG POWERS?

WORST SUPERPOWER EVER!

LEGOO SHOOTS...

TCHAK

THE BLAST ARE LIKE CLOUDS OF GAS! THE PUCK JUST PASSES THROUGH THEM!

HOW ARE THEY EVEN WEARING THOSE HELMETS? OR GLOVES?

GOOODREAU SHOOTS...

OKAY, WHY AREN'T WE PLAYING THE BLAST? I'M PRETTY SURE THE PODS COULD TAKE THEM!

ACTUALLY . . . WE WERE ELIMINATED BY THE BLAST IN ROUND ONE. TWICE.

THREE TIMES.

BECAUSE YOU WERE OVERWHELMED BY THE SMELL?

I THINK WE KNOW WHO'S GOING TO WIN THIS GAME . . .

. . . LET'S GET TO THE CRAG GAME BEFORE WE PASS OUT!

WHOA. THAT'S A CRAG? THEY ARE **HUGE**.

THEY'RE LIKE BOULDERS ON SKATES! IF YOU CAN CALL THOSE SKATES . . .

DOUBLE WHOA. THOSE ARE THE STALKS FROM BAMBOOM? THEY'RE EVEN BIGGER!

THEY'RE TALLER AT LEAST. THEY SHOULD BE PLAYING BASKETBALL!

THIS IS CRAZY-- THEY'RE GIANTS! HOW ARE THE PODS SUPPOSED TO BEAT EITHER OF THESE TEAMS?

HEY, BIGGER DOESN'T MEAN BETTER, YOU KNOW. OR UNBEATABLE.

AND HERE'S THE FACE-OFF!

69

LATER, AT THE SPORKS' PRACTICE

SO, THAT'S OUR COMPETITION, HUH?

AREN'T THEY ADORABLE, ISAAC?

TCHAK

RIGHT... ADORABLE.

ADORABLE, BUT NOT UNBEATABLE.

THESE GUYS ALMOST LOOK LIKE A **REAL** HOCKEY TEAM...

...THEY'VE GOT JERSEYS AND MOST OF THE GEAR EXCEPT FOR A HELMET.

WHY ARE YOU SO **OBSESSED** WITH WHAT EVERYONE IS WEARING?

IT'S JUST WEIRD HOW NO ONE WEARS *ALL* THE USUAL GEAR...

...AND WHY SOME TEAMS WEAR HELMETS WHILE OTHERS DON'T...

...AND SOME PLAYERS DON'T EVEN WEAR SKATES!

YEAH, IT'S KIND OF RANDOM!

BUT MAYBE THEY DON'T MAKE HELMETS IN GIANT-ROCK-PEOPLE SIZE?

MAYBE IF THE LIGHTNING BIRDS WORE JERSEYS, THEY'D CATCH FIRE?

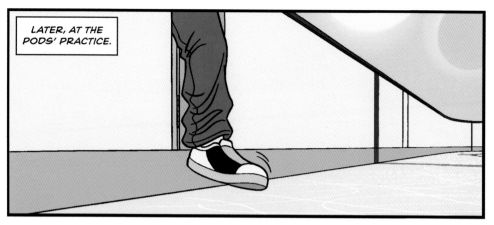

LATER, AT THE PODS' PRACTICE.

WE ARE READY, COACH!

READY WHEN YOU ARE!

UM ... GO AHEAD, YOU GUYS. I, UH, FORGOT SOMETHING ...

EVERYTHING ALL RIGHT, COACH?

YEAH ... I JUST WANTED TO REVIEW A PLAY BEFORE, YOU KNOW ...

ARE YOU SURE YOU'RE ALL RIGHT? YOU'RE SWEATING ...

OH, UM ... MAYBE THOSE MACKEREL JACKS DIDN'T AGREE WITH ME?

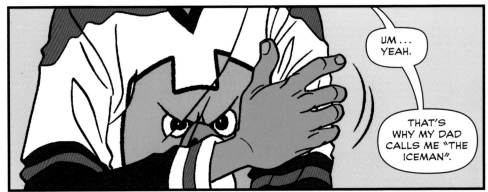

UM . . . YEAH.

THAT'S WHY MY DAD CALLS ME "THE ICEMAN".

CAN'T KEEP ME OFF THE ICE FOR LONG.

HEH.

WHAT'S GOING ON, ISAAC?

UM ... I'LL BE RIGHT BACK, YOU GUYS!

COACH?

WHERE ARE YOU GOING **NOW**?

I'M JUST GOING TO PUT ON MY SKATES.

Chapter 4: HOW THE ROOKIE CRUMBLES

NO ONE FROM OUTSIDE GALAXIA HAS EVER PLAYED IN THE GHL.

WELCOME BACK TO HOCKEY NIGHT IN GALAXIA!

IT'S THE SPORKS FROM CORALINA VERSUS THE ZEAZIDE PODS. LET'S FACE IT, FOLKS, WE KNOW HOW THIS ONE IS GOING TO PLAY OUT.

EVEN THE NHL ON EARTH HAS HAD THIRTY-ONE EXTRATERRESTRIALS PLAY IN ITS LEAGUE SINCE 1947.

THE PODS HAVE COME IN LAST IN EVERY GHL TOURNAMENT, KNOCKED OUT IN THE FIRST ROUND, SO WE DON'T EXPECT THINGS TO BE MUCH DIFFERENT TONIGHT.

UNTIL RECENTLY, ONLY THOSE FROM MOUNT KRAKOOM HAVE PLAYED FOR THE STREEK; THE CRAG HAVE ALL HAILED FROM ROKITH; NO ONE NOT FROM FLATULAND HAS PLAYED FOR THE BLAST AND SO ON . . .

HOWEVER, THE LAST-PLACE PODS SEEM TO BE TRYING SOMETHING NEW...

I ♥ SPORKS!

...KNOW WHERE YOU'RE GOING TO PUT THE PUCK BEFORE YOU EVEN GET IT...

ARE YOU GOING TO PASS? SHOOT? THINK AHEAD, LIKE IN THE VIDEO GAME...

THIS IS EASIER SAID THAN DONE.

WE CAN DO IT, ICABOD. JUST LIKE WE PRACTISED.

JUST LIKE WE PRACTISED WITH ISAAC. HE WILL LEAD US OUT THERE.

UM...RIGHT, ELROD.

SO, LET'S GET OUT THERE AND... DO OUR BEST!

LET'S GO, PODS! LET'S GO!

OWW!

ISAAC? WHAT HAPPENED!?

I, UH, ROLLED MY ANKLE ... OW ... THAT WAS REALLY CLUMSY OF ME ... SORRY.

SHALL I CALL A ROBOT MEDIC?

NO, NO, IT'S NOT THAT BAD ... I'LL BE OKAY. BUT ... I DON'T THINK I CAN PLAY.

ELROD, SUB FOR ME, OKAY?

I THOUGHT YOU WERE GOING TO PLAY? NOT JUST "COACH" FROM THE BENCH.

I WAS PLANNING TO ... BUT NOW I CAN'T. MY ANKLE ...

PREDICTABLE.

YOU GOT THIS, PODS!

JUST LIKE WE PRACTISED...

HERE'S THE FACEOFF...

...PASS TO CENTRE...

TOC

...STICKENHEISER SHOOTS!

...AND THE SPORKS HAVE THE PUCK...

COME ON, YOU GUYS! GO GET HIM!

NICE SAVE BY THE ALIEN NETMINDER!

TCHAK

NO SCORE AT THE END OF THE FIRST PERIOD, BUT THE SPORKS ARE LEADING WITH TEN SHOTS ON GOAL VERSUS THE PODS' ONE.

LILY IS DOING AMAZING OUT THERE!

BUT YOU GUYS CAN'T EXPECT HER TO DO ALL THE WORK ...

AT LEAST THEY'RE **OUT THERE** WITH ME.

UM ... LET'S TURN IT UP A BIT. STOP LOOKING LIKE YOU'RE SCARED OF THE SPORKS.

STILL NO SCORE AFTER TWO PERIODS, AND IT LOOKS LIKE THE PODS MIGHT BE DOWN A PLAYER OR TWO...

WHY DIDN'T ANYONE TELL ME ABOUT THE SPORKS' SPIKY PUFFERFISH HEADS?

IT DOESN'T MATTER NOW, DOES IT? I DON'T THINK ELROD AND JAROD CAN PLAY.

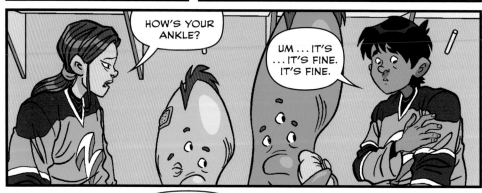

HOW'S YOUR ANKLE?

UM...IT'S ...IT'S FINE. IT'S FINE.

WE'RE SHORT A PLAYER. **YOU** HAVE TO GET OUT THERE!

IT IS AN HONOUR TO BE PLAYING WITH THE GOAT.

WE HAVE A CHANCE NOW!

JUST LIKE WE PRACTISED, RIGHT, ISAAC?

THE PODS ARE PLAYING BOTH THEIR ALIEN RINGERS NOW, LET'S SEE HOW THIS PLAYS OUT.

CLAC

PODS WIN THE DRAW!

THE ALIEN HAS THE PUCK ...

GULP!

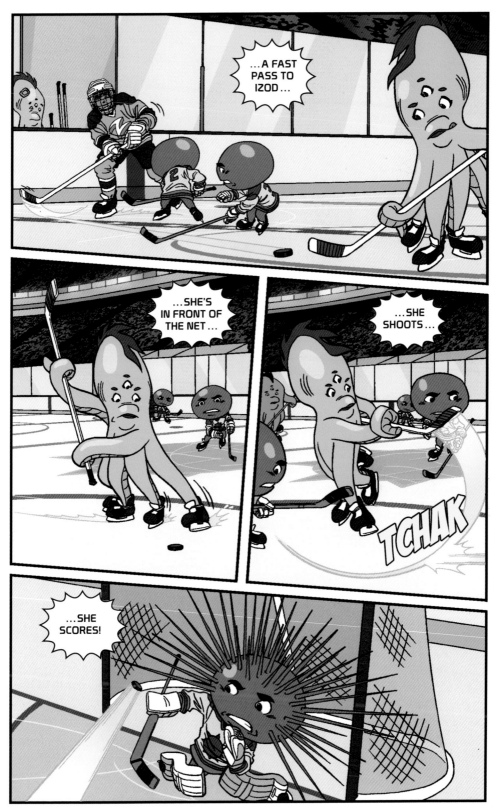

IN A STUNNING UPSET, THE PODS BEAT THE SPORKS 1–0, ENDING THEIR EMBARRASSING DECADE-LONG LOSING STREAK!

1 – 0

AND SPEAKING OF STREEKS, IT WILL BE THE TEAM FROM MOUNT KRAKOOM TAKING ON THE PODS IN THE NEXT ROUND...

WE DID IT, YOU GUYS!

YOU DID IT WITH YOUR STATE-OF-THE-ART COACHING TECHNIQUES!

NO, **IZOD** DID IT WITH HER WICKED SLAPSHOT!

AND OF COURSE **LILY** WITH THE SHUTOUT!

96

THIS WAS ALL A BIG MISTAKE! SKOU7 WAS LOOKING FOR AN ACTUAL **GOAT.** NOT FOR ME.

GOAT? THERE'S SOMETHING WRONG WITH THAT ROBOT. HE DOESN'T EVEN KNOW GRILLED-CHEESE SANDWICHES HAVE **CHEESE** IN THEM.

ANYWAY, I WANTED TO TELL YOU FIRST. BEFORE I TOLD THE REST OF THE TEAM.

TELL THEM WHAT? LOOK AT THEM, THEY'RE PUMPED! THEY'RE READY TO TAKE ON THE **WORLD!**

DON'T TAKE THAT AWAY FROM THEM. **GO WITH IT.** SO YOU'RE NOT THE GOAT. YOU WILL BE IN THEIR EYES IF YOU HELP THEM WIN AGAIN.

AND EVEN IF WE DON'T WIN? THIS WAS NO MISTAKE. THIS WAS AN **OPPORTUNITY...**

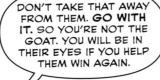

MAYBE YOU'RE RIGHT. I MAY NOT BE THE GREATEST OF ALL TIME, BUT I **CAN** PLAY HOCKEY. AND I'M PRETTY GOOD.

PLUS, I'M A **CHAMPION** ONLINE!

SO...IT IS THE MUCK VERSUS THE STALKS AND THE STREEK VERSUS THE PODS IN THE TOURNAMENT SEMIFINALS.

THINGS JUST GOT *INTERESTING!* I LIKE THIS!

GHL

SADLY, THE BLAST ARE IN LAST PLACE, SIRE.

CURSES! WHAT WILL MY LAUNDRY SMELL LIKE WHEN IT GETS BACK FROM FLATULAND?

ANYWAY, I GUESS THOSE ALIENS ARE WORKING OUT FOR THE PODS?

IT APPEARS SO, SIRE.

IT SEEMS TO IMPROVE THE GAME, SO PERHAPS WE SHOULD ENCOURAGE *EVERYONE* TO RECRUIT NEW PLAYERS, CHANGE THEIR ROSTER OR OTHERWISE **MIX** THINGS UP...

HERE WE GO, FOLKS!

FACEOFF! THE STREEK GET THE PUCK.

...QUICK PASS...

...IN FRONT OF THE NET...

BZZT

TCHAK

...OSTRICHKIN SHOOTS...

IT LOOKS LIKE THE PODS ARE GAINING CONFIDENCE, WHILE THE STREEK ARE GETTING FRUSTRATED AND STARTING TO LOSE THEIR COOL.

TWEET

THAT'S A TWO-MINUTE PENALTY FOR CROSS-CHECKING!

POWER PLAY, YOU GUYS! THIS IS OUR CHANCE!

THE STREEK SEEM TO BE SLOWING DOWN.

WE ARE **ALL** SLOWING DOWN!

IT'S THE ICE! IT'S GETTING SOFTER. THERE'S ALWAYS A SUPER-THIN LAYER OF WATER ON THE ICE, BUT I THINK THE STREEK'S ELECTRICITY IS MAKING IT THICKER ...

AND MAYBE WE CAN USE THAT TO OUR ADVANTAGE. OR AT LEAST YOU ZEAZIDERS CAN. TAKE OFF YOUR SKATES!

EXCUSE ME?

EXCUSE US? HOW ARE WE SUPPOSED TO SKATE?

YOU'RE NOT -- YOU'RE GOING TO **HYDROPLANE!**

THIS IS INTERESTING, FOLKS ... THE STREEK ARE **LESS** ONE PLAYER SO THE PODS HAVE THE POWER PLAY ...

... BUT THEY ARE PLAYING IT **LESS** THEIR SKATES!

IZOD GOES BEHIND THE NET ...

... PASSES THE PUCK TO ELROD ...

FLYZERMAN CAN'T KEEP UP WITH ELROD!

HE'S IN FRONT OF THE NET...

...HE SHOOTS...

TCHAK

...AND SCORES! WHAT A PLAY! WE ARE NOW TIED! WHAT A PLAY!

HY-DRO-PLANE! HY-DRO-PLANE! HY-DRO-PLANE!

WE'RE GOING TO THE FINALS!

MAYBE THIS **IS** A DREAM!

IT'S A DREAM COME TRUE FOR US!

IS THIS REALLY HAPPENING?

YES, IT IS.

CONGRATULATIONS, PODS. YOU REALLY ARE PLAYING IN THE FINALS. IN FACT, YOU'LL BE PLAYING IN THE FINALS...

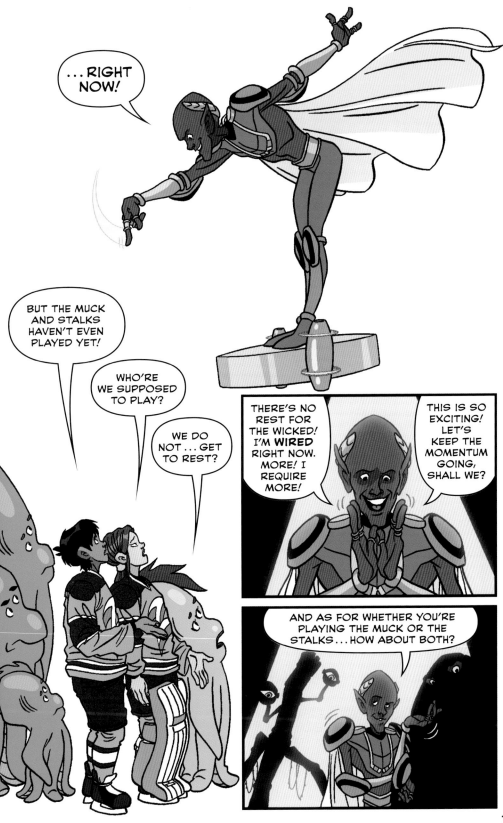

111

CHAPTER 6 ONE

THE GOAT

AND THAT'S HOW THE FIRST ANNUAL GHL ALL-STAR GAME CAME ABOUT. THE VERY BEST GALAXIAN PLAYERS FACING OFF AGAINST A SOMEWHAT TIRED INTERGALACTIC TEAM.

THE GALAXIANS CHARGE INTO ENEMY TERRITORY ...

ZZT

BZZ

UGH!

IT'S OKAY, LIL. WE'RE ONLY DOWN TWO GOALS. STILL A PERIOD TO GO.

HOW ARE WE SUPPOSED TO DEFEND AGAINST THESE GUYS?

YOU KNOW WHAT THEY SAY: THE BEST DEFENCE IS A GOOD OFFENCE.

THEY'RE USING EVERY ADVANTAGE THEY HAVE ON US--WHETHER IT'S THEIR SIZE OR THEIR POWERS OR WHATEVER...

...SO LET'S TAKE ADVANTAGE OF THOSE ADVANTAGES!

YOU SOUND LIKE YOU HAVE SOME IDEAS, SO HERE...

IS THIS **REALLY** A GOODTIME TO BE PLAYING VIDEO GAMES, LILY?

IT'S NOT VIDEO GAMES ...IT'S STATE OF THE ART COACHING!

OKAY PODS, WE'RE GOING TO SHAKE THINGS UP A BIT. FOR STARTERS, I WANT TODD COVERING THE STALK...

BUT HE IS TEN TIMES MY HEIGHT!

EXACTLY!

HERE'S WHAT I WANT YOU TO DO...

119

THE GALAXIAN ALL-STARS WERE SHARP, SCORING GOALS IN THE FIRST AND SECOND PERIODS. BUT IT CAME DOWN TO TWO BRILLIANT PLAYS IN THE THIRD.

THE PODS AND THEIR ALIENS ARE RUNNING OUT OF TIME, FOLKS.

IT'S ISAAC WITH THE FAKE...

121

IT'S A NAIL-BITER, FOLKS! LESS THAN A MINUTE ON THE CLOCK AND THE PODS TRAIL BY ONE.

TODD PASSES...

TOC

...HE SLIPS! AND HE SLIDES -- RIGHT BETWEEN GROOTZKY'S STALKS!

NOW IT'S ISAAC WITH A QUICK PASS...

...TODD SHOOTS!

TCHAK

HE SCORES! IT'S A TIE GAME, FOLKS! A TIE!

WHEN REGULATION TIME ENDS, THE EMPORER'S RULE IS: SHOOTOUT!

NO OVERTIME! IT'S A CONTROVERSIAL, DUBIOUS, OH-SO-EXCITING RULE. JUST THE WAY THE EMPEROR LIKES IT... AND KIND OF LIKE THE EMPEROR HIMSELF.

CROWSBY'S GOT THE FIRST ALL-STARS ATTEMPT...

...SAVED BY THE ALIEN NETMINDER!

BZZT

ELROD TAKES THE PODS' FIRST SHOT...

TOC

...AND HE'S DENIED BY SAWCHUNK!

STICKENHEISER'S GOT THE SECOND SHOT FOR THE ALL-STARS...

...SAVED!

IZOD SHOOTS...

...NO SCORE AFTER FOUR!

127

SO, CONGRATULATIONS ONCE AGAIN, PODS! NOT ONLY DID YOU WIN THE CHAMPIONSHIP BUT YOU WIN "MOST IMPROVED PLAYER"... ALL OF YOU!

THERE'S ONLY ONE PLAQUE SO YOU'LL HAVE TO FIGHT FOR IT OR SHARE IT OR SOMETHING. I HEAR YOU PODS ARE GOOD WITH THE WHOLE SHARING THING.

AS FOR YOU ALIENS, YOU MADE THE GAME SO MUCH MORE EXCITING! SO MUCH MORE ENTERTAINING! SO MUCH MORE ENGAGING! SO MUCH SO...

...I PRONOUNCE YOU HONORARY GALAXIAN CITIZENS!

WHOA. THAT'S... THAT'S AMAZING! THANK YOU!

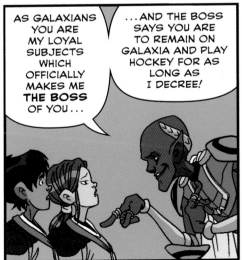

AS GALAXIANS YOU ARE MY LOYAL SUBJECTS WHICH OFFICIALLY MAKES ME **THE BOSS** OF YOU...

...AND THE BOSS SAYS YOU ARE TO REMAIN ON GALAXIA AND PLAY HOCKEY FOR AS LONG AS I DECREE!

WAIT... WHAT? THAT IS **SO** NOT AMAZING! NO THANK YOU!

THAT WAS **NOT** PART OF THE DEAL. YOU SAID WE COULD GO HOME...

I AM THE RULER OF ALL THINGS. I AM THE HOCKEY COMMISSIONER. **I AM THE #1 HOCKEY FAN IN THE UNIVERSE...**

AND I SAY YOU STAY!

BOO!

HISS!

DOWN WITH MAROON!

LET THEM GO!

FREE THE ALIENS!

OUCH! STOP THAT! I SAID, THROW **MONEY**...NOT ROCKCORN! AND CERTAINLY NOT MACKEREL JACKS!

I WILL PUT YOU **ALL** IN THE PENALTY BOX OF PAIN!

JUST **TRY** TO FIT EVERYONE IN THERE...NO DEAL!

HEY, WHAT IF WE MADE OUR **OWN** DEAL?

DOES IT INVOLVE GRILLED-CHEESE SANDWICHES? BECAUSE I'M NOT AGREEING TO ANOTHER ONE OF THOSE DEALS...

WHAT IF WE PROMISED TO COME BACK AND PLAY IN NEXT YEAR'S TOURNAMENT?

DEAL! I DECREE IT EVEN! I DECREE IT, YOU HEAR ME?

130

THE NEXT DAY.

I GUESS THIS IS GOODBYE?

GOODBYE FOR NOW?

JUST GOODBYE FOR NOW. I'LL MISS YOU GUYS. BUT I'M ALSO KIND OF GLAD TO BE GOING BACK HOME ... EVEN THOUGH IT'S NOT MY OLD HOME.

WE THANK YOU SO MUCH FOR EVERYTHING YOU HAVE DONE FOR US. YOU HAVE MADE OUR DREAM COME TRUE ...

AW, YOU GUYS. I'M GLAD WE WERE ABLE TO SHARE THIS DREAM. AND WE CAN'T WAIT TO PLAY WITH YOU AGAIN IN THE NEXT TOURNAMENT!

RIGHT, ISAAC?

ISAAC!

WHAT'S THE RUSH? *SKOU7* CAN BEND SPACE AND TIME OR WHATEVER AND GET US HOME PRETTY MUCH WHEN WE LEFT SO ...

...I'M NOT GOING HOME YET!

I WAS PROMISED A BEACH VACATION!

LIKE MOST KIDS, ISAAC HAS HAD HIS SHARE OF ACCIDENTS...

...BUT NONE WAS MORE INCREDIBLE THAN THE THE UNFORTUNATE ACCIDENT WHICH LED TO THE UNLIKELY MIX-UP...

...WHICH LED TO HIM PLAYING HOCKEY ON ANOTHER PLANET AGAINST AN ALL-STAR ALIEN TEAM, AND BECOMING THE GREATEST OF ALL TIME...

FOR NOW... THAT WILL ALL CHANGE NEXT YEAR, WHEN **THIS GOAT** GETS IN THE GAME! UNTIL THEN, I'M HEADING TO THE ALL-YOU-CAN-EAT GARBAGE BUFFET.

THE END.

GHL hockey cards are out of this world!

J. TORRES is a Filipino Canadian writer perhaps best known for his work on the Shuster Award winning Teen Titans Go comic book. He has written characters from A (Archies) to Z (The Mighty Zodiac) plus Batman, Black Panther, Rugrats, Simpsons, WALL-E, Wonder Woman, the X-Men and many more in between. His graphic novels include the Eisner Award listed *Alison Dare*, Junior Library Guild selection *Bigfoot Boy*, Parents Choice Award winning *Brobots*, Junior Library Guild selection *How to Spot a Sasquatch*, and the YALSA listed *Lola: A Ghost Story*. He lives just outside of "Hogtown" with his wife and two sons.

TIM LEVINS studied Fine Art and Classical Animation before breaking into the comic book business in the mid-1990s. Tim is best known for his work on the Eisner Award-winning DC Comics series Batman: Gotham Adventures. Over the years, he has illustrated many other titles for DC, Marvel Comics and Archie Comics, and has drawn several children's books, including the *Scooby-Doo! Encyclopedia*. Tim enjoys life in Midland, Ontario, with his wife, son, and two dogs.